LEARNING TO LIVE SERIES

LIVING BY HIS GRACE

NAVPRESS ®

A MINISTRY OF THE NAVIGATORS
P.O. Box 6000, Colorado Springs, Colorado 80934

The Navigators is an international Christian organization. Jesus Christ gave His followers the Great Commission to go and make disciples (Matthew 28:19). The aim of The Navigators is to help fulfill that commission by multiplying laborers for Christ in every nation.

NavPress is the publishing ministry of The Navigators. NavPress publications are tools to help Christians grow. Although publications alone cannot make disciples or change lives, they can help believers learn biblical discipleship, and apply what they learn to their lives and ministries.

© 1987 The Navigators Great Britain
All rights reserved, including translation
ISBN: 0-89109-057-6
10579

Printed in the United States of America

Contents

Author

The LEARNING TO LIVE series was written by Peter Dowse. Born in Great Britain, he has degrees from Cambridge University and London Bible College. Peter has been on staff with The Navigators since 1977. He led the student ministry at Sheffield University for several years, and now gives his time to writing and speaking.

Make the Most of This Bible Study

We live in a world of shifting values and conflicting viewpoints. Is it possible in the midst of this to know what is right and what is true? Yes it is! For God is true, and He has chosen to give us in the Bible a definitive expression of His own mind and will, His knowledge of reality, and His thoughts and plans for the world.

> *You will know the truth,*
> *and the truth will set you free.*
> (JOHN 8:32)

It is the aim of this Bible study series to introduce you to the joy and privilege of digging out that truth for yourself.

Personal Bible study is demanding. You will need to give it much time and serious endeavor. In this series, each lesson takes two to three hours to prepare. The rewards of personal Bible study, however, are great. You will surely discover this for yourself as you complete the books in this series.

Remember that Bible study is not merely an academic exercise. You will need to think, but don't forget that the Bible is God's Word. Pray before you start each lesson. Ask God to help you understand the truths and make you sensitive to what He wants to say to you through a particular lesson. Pray as you study, "Lord, what does this mean? How does this relate to

5

me?" Praise Him when you discover something that excites you. The fruit of Bible study should not be just increased head knowledge; it should produce a deeper relationship with God and a lifestyle that is more honoring to Him.

If you can find others who are willing to put in the time to do personal preparation, you will find great value in meeting together to discuss each lesson. But don't let the absence of such a group deter you. Get into God's Word for yourself. You won't be disappointed.

> *When your words came, I ate them;*
> *they were my joy and my heart's delight.*
> (JEREMIAH 15:16)

SOME EXPLANATIONS: The definitions given throughout this series are, of necessity, brief. More exhaustive definitions of the words can be found in any good Bible dictionary, for example, *The Illustrated Bible Dictionary*, published by Inter-Varsity Press.

Whenever the name of a person who has been quoted is followed by an asterisk, you will find information about that person in "Who's Who" on page 115.

Additional references are listed for some questions. They are optional references that you can use if you want to. For an example, see question 8 on page 51.

Each lesson has sections entitled "Ask Yourself." These do not require written responses, though you may want to write answers to the questions in a notebook. Each lesson also has a section entitled "For Further Study." These sections are optional.

The six books in the *Learning to Live* series can be done in any order, or you can follow this suggested sequence:

Clarifying Your Commitment
Living by His Grace
Living in the World
Disciplines of Living
Your Part in His Plan
Standing Firm

Guidance for Growth

In this book we will look closely at how God wants us to grow now that we are Christians. But first, we must understand who we are, for until we are sure of that, change is a threatening prospect. We ask ourselves, What will be left of me if I allow Christ to dominate my life? Examining the Bible's teaching about God's purposes can calm our fears.

An understanding of the grace of God and the ministry of the Holy Spirit can deliver us from a proud man-centered approach to change. We must make sure we are not pursuing a program of do-it-yourself reformation.

The principles of growth in these lessons are vital. As we remind ourselves of God's great purposes, we are able to see obedience and discipleship in a positive way. As we reflect on the grace of God, we can rest secure in who we are and be honest about our need to change. As we learn to live by God's Spirit and conform to His Word, we can progressively be renewed in the image of Christ. In all of this, our relationships with other Christians are both a stimulus to growth and a foretaste of eternity.

Living as God Intends

Who am I? What am I worth? Where am I going? Some modern
thinkers have given very negative answers: man is "a naked
ape," "a meaningless cog," "a useless passion." Though they
might not go along with such conclusions, many people are
searching, consciously or unconsciously, for a sense of value
and a reason for living. The Bible provides both. In God's Word,
we discover that we are valuable because God made us. And
there is a reason for living because He has a purpose for us. To
live life to the full, we need to understand these truths and
live as God intends.

In this lesson we examine God's original purpose in creating
mankind, and we see how mankind fell away from that purpose. Then we consider the marvelous way God has rescued us
through Christ. Finally, we reflect upon God's determined purpose to renew us in the image of Christ, and thereby to re-
store us to what He intends us to be. To understand God's
unchanging intentions is to find meaning and direction.

Pause for Prayer

The truths we are considering in this lesson are so vast that it
is tempting to focus only on academic understanding. Pray
that God will not allow you to fall into that trap. Ask Him to
enable you to see the implications for your daily living as well.

Creation

Before you consider the questions, read Genesis 1 and 2 to get an overview of God's work of creation.

There is insufficient space here to discuss the issues involved in interpreting these early chapters of Genesis, in particular, their relationship with current scientific theories of man's origin. However, we must not allow debate concerning the detailed interpretation of these accounts to rob us of their great central truths. These chapters describe real events that are fundamental to our whole understanding of humanity.

---

1. Focus on Genesis 1:20-31, which describes the creation of living creatures.
   a. Compare the following verses and then list ways in which man is like the animals.

   Verses 21 and 25 with verses 26 and 27

   Verse 22 with verse 28

Verse 29 with verse 30

b. Now look at verses 28-30 and list those things that indicate that man is different from the animals.

---

2. Read Genesis 2:15-25. How do these verses illustrate the uniqueness of man in the following areas?

a. His relationship with God

b. His role in creation

c. His responsibility to make moral choices

d. His relationships with others

---

3. Reflect on the following verses in Genesis. What do they reveal about God's attitude toward man?

1:28-29

2:8-9

2:15-16

ASK YOURSELF: **a.** What have I learned from Genesis 1 and 2 about man's worth, security, and purpose? **b.** What have I learned from these chapters about the nature and character of God?

The Fall
Read through Genesis 3, which describes the fall of man.

---

4. Refer to verses 1-6 for the following questions.

   a. How did the serpent go about tempting Eve? (In the New Testament, the serpent represents Satan. See Revelation 12:9.)

   b. What was Eve's response to the serpent's tempting?

c. How did Adam react?

d. What can you learn from this incident about the nature of sin?

"Transgression meant the repudiation of His authority, doubt of His goodness, dispute with His wisdom, rejection of His justice, contradiction of His veracity, and the spurning of His grace."[1]
—JOHN MURRAY

---

5. Read again Genesis 3:7-19. What consequences of sin are seen in those areas of life that before the Fall marked man as unique?

a. His relationship with God (verses 8-10)

b. His role in creation (verses 14-19)

c. His willingness to take responsibility for moral choices (verses 11-13)

d. His relationship with his wife (verses 7 and 16)

The serpent promised that Adam and Eve would become like God. Actually, they became unlike the human beings they were meant to be. Although it was not destroyed, the image of God in man was distorted and marred. Man as we know him today is not what God intends him to be.

---

6. Reflect on Genesis 3:21-24. What does it reveal of God's character in regard to sin and grace?

New Creation

The record of the first disobedience by man has much to teach us about temptation and sin. That first sin also had a unique importance for the human race.

---

7. Read Romans 5:12, 15-19.

a. In the chart below, list the consequences for all men because of Adam's disobedience. Then, for each consequence list the effect that Christ can have.

Consequence of Adam's sin	Effect of Christ's gift

b. Based on Romans 5:19 and 7:15-24, what do you think it means to say that every human being is a sinner?

c. Look again at Romans 5:15. How would you explain the phrase "the grace of the one man, Jesus Christ"?

O loving wisdom of our God, when all was sin and shame,
A second Adam to the fight, and to the rescue came.
O wisest love! that flesh and blood which did in Adam fail,
Should strive afresh against the foe,
should strive and should prevail.
—JOHN HENRY NEWMAN*
"Praise to the Holiest"

Whereas the man Adam disobeyed at the first point of choice, the man Jesus Christ was "obedient to death" (Philippians 2:8). As the representative of fallen humanity, He "died for sins once for all" (1 Peter 3:18). Yet He Himself was "without sin" (Hebrews 4:15). Thus, "it was impossible for death to keep its hold on him" (Acts 2:24). By rising from the dead, He made a new beginning for humanity, free from the effects of the Fall.

Here and now, by faith, we can become a part of this new beginning: "Therefore, if anyone is in Christ, he is a new creation" (2 Corinthians 5:17).

---

8. Read 1 Corinthians 15:21-23 and 45-57.

   a. In these verses, what similarities and contrasts do you find between Adam and Christ?

   b. Describe the future for those who are in Christ.

The term *spiritual* in this passage does not mean nonphysical. The main point in 1 Corinthians 15 is that there is a resurrection of the body. The word *spiritual* probably means "adapted to the life of the Spirit." We will not spend eternity as disembodied spirits. On the contrary, our future experience is to be that of full humanity freed from the dehumanizing presence of sin. In a sense, eternity is a restoration of the experience God intended for Adam and Eve. It is more than this, however, for it is human experience free from any possibility of sin or death.

For Further Study

The early chapters of Romans focus on the way in which we all fall short of God's standards and stand guilty before Him. Lesson 3 of *Clarifying Your Commitment* is a study of the marvelous way in which God, through Christ, is able to acquit us and count us as righteous. The later chapters of Romans expose a deeper problem: we are sinners not merely by conduct, but by nature. Read Romans 5:12-14 and 20-21. God's law identifies and exposes sinful conduct and attitudes. But these are only the symptoms of a sinful nature.

A. Read Romans 7:7-12. How does God deal with our sinful nature?

B. Read carefully Romans 6:3-14. The passage describes an "old self" and (by implication) a "new self."

Our old self is descended from Adam and is therefore sub-ject to all the consequences of Adam's sin. What happens to our old self when we become a Christian?

Verse 7 says that we are "freed [literally, justified] from sin." Read Romans 7:1-4 and then explain what you think this means.

What basis do we have for believing that we can survive this process and that a new self can emerge?

What does the future hold for our new self?

Until our death and/or Christ's return, our new self must continue to live in a fallen human body with its sinful nature. How does this affect our new self?

What is the appropriate response to this condition?

Note: Romans 7 goes on to stress the fierceness of the battle with our sinful nature, and Romans 8 stresses the ministry of the Holy Spirit in enabling us to win day to day. We will study this further in lesson 3, "Living Through His Spirit."

New Attitude

An understanding of God's purposes should affect our daily living.

9. Read Ephesians 4:20-24.

    a. Focus on verse 24, along with Colossians 3:9-10. How are

God's purpose in salvation and His purpose in creation linked together?

b. Still keeping in mind Ephesians 4:24, read Romans 8:28-29. What is our new model for being God-like in character?

---

10. Read verses 20-24 of Ephesians 4 again.

a. According to this passage, what is central to living a new life?

b. How can an understanding of the true nature of our old self (verse 22) and our new self (verse 24) help us?

"(Becoming holy) . . . is essentially an affirmation of life. The whole purpose of the Christian life is the recovery of the original image of God, in other words, the recovery of the kind of human experience which God intended Adam and Eve to have before the Fall. . . . [The Bible] points us back to the path of life our first ancestors were designed to walk on. . . . Therefore, when I seek to obey God's commandments, I am not working against myself, but for myself. I am acting in accordance with my nature as the image of God. As I do what is right, I establish my true identity: I free myself!"[2] — RANALD MACAULAY and JERRAM BARRS

ASK YOURSELF: a. How can these truths in Ephesians 4 help me to be wholeheartedly committed to God, rather than to be resistant to His desire to change me? **b.** In what areas am I resisting God's renewing work by being true to my old self?

Stop, Think, and Pray

If our lives are to change, our thinking must change. How has your thinking changed as a result of this lesson? Perhaps you have gained a deeper understanding of the nature of man, both as he was intended to be and as he now is. Or perhaps you have learned some things about the nature of God and His purposes. Ask God to help you clarify what you have learned and to help you change your attitude toward life. God may be speaking to you about a specific area of life in which you are (perhaps unconsciously) resisting His work of renewal. Put your thoughts in writing.

How my understanding has deepened

How this should affect my life

What specific action is needed

One way to remember the truths you have studied is to choose key Bible verses and memorize them. You can select your own verses from the passages you study, or memorize the one suggested at the end of each lesson. (See page 113 for help in memorizing Scripture.)

Suggested memory verse about living as God intends

> **You were taught, with regard to your former way of life, to put off your old self, which is being corrupted by its deceitful desires; to be made new in the attitude of your minds; and to put on the new self, created to be like God in true righteousness and holiness.** (Ephesians 4:22-24)

NOTES: 1. John Murray, *New Bible Dictionary* (Leicester, England: InterVarsity Press, 1962), page 1190.

2. Ranald Macaulay and Jerram Barrs, *Christianity with a Human Face* (Leicester, England: InterVarsity Press, 1978), pages 16 and 20.

Living by God's Grace

In the previous lesson, "Living as God Intends," we saw how God created man "in his own image." Endowed with unique personal qualities, and created to be the object of God's special affection, man could not help but be aware of his significance and value to the Creator. God also gave man a special role in His world and thereby provided purpose for his life. In turning away from God and putting himself at the center, man lost his relationship with God and his hope of eternal life. This, in turn, cast its shadow over man's daily life, bringing insecurity, purposelessness, and fear.

God's love is not to be stopped, however. In Christ we see God's plan to redeem man from the consequences of sin. In one sense, this redemption is complete, for our sins have been forgiven and our relationship with God has been restored. We have become new in Christ, destined to spend eternity with God.

In another sense, our redemption is future, for only when Christ returns will we be completely free from the presence of sin in our lives and in our environment.

In yet another sense, our redemption is ongoing. God is at work now renewing us in the image of Christ. He is progressively delivering us from the effects of the Fall. In this lesson, we will see how Christ's work has reaffirmed our value and significance to God, and provided us with the security for confident living and courageous service.

Pause for Prayer

As Christians, we have the immense privilege of enjoying a restored relationship with God. We can know His companionship in all that we do. Nonetheless, it is our natural (fallen) inclination to live independently of Him. It is even possible to complete a Bible study without involving God. But to do so is to miss the heart of it. Be sure you don't rush through this lesson as an exercise in comprehension. Take time to talk over what you are studying with the Author.

The Riches of God's Grace

Before answering questions 1-5, it would help you to read the first three chapters of Ephesians. Notice how often grace is mentioned. The phrase *the heavenly realms* refers to the unseen world of spiritual reality. The phrase occurs five times in Ephesians (the *New International Version*), but nowhere else in Paul's letters.

GRACE: God's undeserved favor; His unmerited love.

---

1. Focus on Ephesians 1:3-14.

   a. How has God taken the initiative in bringing about our salvation?

   b. What are the consequences for us of God's work?

c. Verses 12 and 14 speak of "the praise of His glory." In light of the rest of the passage, why is this such an appropriate description of our purpose in life?

d. What do you think it means in practice to live to the praise of God's glory?

2. Read Ephesians 2:1-10. Then answer the questions in the chart. (Titus 3:3-8 is a good cross-reference.)

What is man's condition by nature? Verses 1-3	What can man's condition be through Christ? Verses 5-6,10

3. Write Ephesians 2:6-9 in your own words. (This technique, called paraphrasing, is a good way to discover how well you understand a passage.)

"The grace of God does not find men fit for salvation, but makes them so." —AUGUSTINE*

"Grace, sit down! You're not the 'God's Grace' the pastor's talking about!"

4. a. What does Ephesians 3:7-8 reveal about the attitude of the Apostle Paul concerning God's grace? (Also read 1 Timothy 1:12-17.)

b. How does Paul describe his ministry in Ephesians 3:2?

5. Paul prayed for the Christians in Ephesus. Read his prayers in Ephesians 1:15-23 and 3:14-21.

a. What did Paul ask for the Ephesian believers?

1:17

1:18-19

b. Based on these requests, what should our focus be in living the Christian life?

ASK YOURSELF: **a**. If a person does not see the need to be "saved by grace," what is faulty in their view of God and of themselves? **b**. How can I more fully express to God my gratitude for His grace?

Standing in Grace
The context for questions 6 and 7 is found in Romans 5:1-11.

---

6. Look at verses 6-10.

a. What does Christ's death demonstrate about God's love for us?

b. How will this affect God's attitude toward us when we face the last Judgment?

"No unsuspected weakness in our characters can come to light to turn God away from us, since He knew us utterly before we knew Him and called us to Himself in the full knowledge of everything that was against us."[1] — A.W. TOZER

---

7. In Romans 5:1-2 we read that we are accepted by God ("have been justified") and will ultimately be received into heaven ("the hope of the glory of God"). The verses also include implications for our day-to-day relationship with God.

   a. What do you think is implied in verse 1 by the statement, "We have peace with God"? (Also see Romans 8:33.)

b. What do you think is implied in verse 2 by the statement, "We have gained access . . . into this grace"? (Also see Romans 8:31-32.)

c. Verse 2 also speaks of "this grace in which we now stand." How can you tell whether or not you are standing in grace?

For Further Study

Because we know that God loves us and wholly accepts us, we should rest secure in our unique value. Often, though, we link our sense of worth to other factors.

A. Listed below and on page 36 are a few such factors. What is the right attitude to have toward each one?

- Physical attractiveness (Psalm 139:13-16)

- Intelligence, strength, or wealth (Jeremiah 9:23-24)

- Marital status (1 Corinthians 7:7)

- Gifts and abilities (1 Corinthians 12:4-7)

- Social status of job (Colossians 3:23-24)

B. According to 2 Corinthians 10:12 and Galatians 6:4-5, what is one prevalent, but false, basis for evaluation?

C. What do the following verses teach about our value and worth to God?

Isaiah 43:1-4

Matthew 10:29-31

ASK YOURSELF: As I look at the ways I think and behave, what indications are there that, in some measure, I believe my security and significance are based on my performance rather than on God's grace?

Living by Grace
As background for questions 8-10, read 1 John 1:5-2:2.

8. Focus on 1 John 1:5-6.

a. God is gracious toward us. What is also true of His character?

b. How does this expose someone who claims to accept God's gracious forgiveness through Christ, and yet makes no attempt to deal with sin in his life?

---

9. Look at 1 John 1:8-10 and 2:1-2.

   a. How should a true Christian deal with sin in his life?

   b. Why is he free to do so?

10. Read 1 John 1:7.

    a. How would you define what it means to "walk in the light"?

    b. This verse mentions two consequences of walking in the light. Why do you think they are related?

"Pride, our natural disposition, which is self-protective, self-righteous and vainglorious, will either refuse to admit failure at all or refuse to try again, lest the trauma of failure be repeated; but the humility of the man who lives by being forgiven knows no such inhibitions."[2] —J.I. PACKER

ASK YOURSELF: a. What indications do I see in my thoughts, feelings, and actions that my understanding of God's grace is inadequate? b. How can I learn to experience God's grace throughout the day and, as a result, live above my failures?

Stop, Think, and Pray

Paul wrote to the Colossian Christians, "All over the world this gospel is producing fruit and growing, just as it has been doing among you since the day you heard it and understood God's grace in all its truth" (Colossians 1:6).

How my understanding of God's grace has deepened

How this will affect my attitude toward life

A specific action I need to take

Suggested memory verse about living by God's grace

**Therefore, since we have been justified through
faith, we have peace with God through our Lord
Jesus Christ, through whom we have gained access
by faith into this grace in which we now stand.
And we rejoice in the hope of the glory of God.
(Romans 5:1-2)**

NOTES: 1. A.W. Tozer, *Knowledge of the Holy* (New York: Harper & Row Publishers, 1961), page 63.
2. J.I. Packer, *God's Words* (Leicester, England: InterVarsity Press, 1981), page 106.

Living Through God's Spirit

In the previous lesson, we focused on God's great and gracious purposes. His generous love for man could not be thwarted by the Fall. Through Christ, God offers pardon to undeserving rebels. He shows us warm personal favor. And He places us eternally in the circle of His love.

How are we actually brought into the living relationship with Jesus Christ from which all else flows? The answer lies in the work of the Holy Spirit. It is He who places us in Christ, thereby securing our present pardon, the restoration of our relationship with God, and the guarantee of future glory. It is He who renews us in the image of Christ. In this lesson, we will examine His work and see how we can actively cooperate with Him.

Pause for Prayer

We study the Bible in the presence of the living God. Each time it is as if He is handing us a love letter from Himself. He stays with us while we read it and waits for our reply. Recognize God's presence as you begin your study. And take time as you work your way through the lesson to reply to what He says.

Who Is the Holy Spirit?

The Bible represents God as a Trinity, consisting of Father, Son, and Holy Spirit. Although the term *trinity* does not occur in the Bible, it is nevertheless a convenient way of expressing the biblical teaching that God, while indisputably One, is also three distinguishable Persons.

In the Old Testament, the fact that there is only one God is stressed, in marked contrast to the very common belief in many gods. But even in the Old Testament there are hints of a fullness in the Godhead, foreshadowing the New Testament teaching about a Trinity. Beginning at Genesis 1:2, there are over eighty references to the Spirit. Other clues lie in the references to "the angel of the Lord" (Exodus 3:2-6), the predictions of a coming Messiah who could be identified as God (Isaiah 9:6), and the occasions when God refers to Himself in plural terms (Genesis 1:26). But the clearest description of the Spirit's Person and work is found in the New Testament.

The doctrine of the Trinity is not the sort of dogma any manmade religion would have contrived, for it is impossible to explain and systematize, yet is at the center of the Christian faith. Everything that matters about Christianity hangs on the truth of God being Three in One. If Jesus is not God, then our sin against God has nothing to do with Him, and He is in no position to forgive us. Similarly, if the Holy Spirit is not God, then our Christian experience is not truly an experience of God.

The doctrine of the Trinity also communicates something about the centrality of love in God. He is not a lonely God who needs to create or redeem in order to relate. On the contrary, He is fulfilled in His own life. There is within His very being the loving harmony of three distinguishable Persons.

Ultimately, we are surveying something beyond our human experience. This should not surprise us, for we are speaking of God. The only response we can make is to worship Him.

---

1. How do the following references link the Holy Spirit and God?

   Psalm 139:7

Acts 5:3-4

---

2. The Bible implies that the Holy Spirit is a Person. He can be grieved (Ephesians 4:30) and insulted (Hebrews 10:29). He gives guidance and speaks (John 16:13). Most notably, although the Greek work for spirit *(pneuma)* is neuter, in the New Testament the Holy Spirit is referred to as "he," not "it."

Consider the following references. What evidence do you find of God being three Persons?

Matthew 3:16-17

Matthew 28:19

ASK YOURSELF: How should my understanding that the Holy Spirit is one Person of the Trinity affect my attitude toward Him?

Jesus and the Spirit

Jesus: Man of the Spirit

---

3. Throughout the Old Testament there are references to the coming of an ideal King/Servant/Prophet—the Messiah—

who would be uniquely endowed with the Holy Spirit (see Isaiah 11:2, 42:1, and 61:1). All the gospel writers agree that Jesus is that Man.

What do the following verses teach concerning the place of the Spirit in Jesus' life?

Luke 1:30-35

Luke 3:21-22

Luke 4:1-2

Luke 4:14-21

Jesus: Giver of the Spirit

4. a. What did John the Baptist predict about Jesus in Mark 1:7-8?

   b. According to Acts 1:3-5 and 2:1-4, how was this promise first fulfilled?

   c. What was necessary before the Spirit could be given in this way? See John 7:37-39 and Acts 2:32-33.

The Holy Spirit makes personal in our lives what Christ has made available by His death, resurrection, and ascension. Jesus secured a place for us in the age to come. The Spirit gives a foretaste of that age here and now.

Jesus: Focus of the Spirit

Jesus' main teaching about the Holy Spirit can be found in John 14-16, in particular 14:15-18, 14:25-26, 15:26-27, and 16:7-15. These passages are well worth an in-depth study. Read through them now, and then consider the questions below.

---

5. In the following verses, what links do you find between the ministry of the Holy Spirit and Jesus?

14:26

15:26

16:12-15

6. Focus on John 14:16-18.

   a. What relationship is there between the ministry of Jesus and the ministry of the Holy Spirit?

   b. In the Old Testament, the Spirit came upon people for short periods for specific tasks. What does Jesus promise will be true for His disciples?

   c. Explain the new experience of the Spirit that the disciples could expect after Jesus finished His work.

   d. In light of this, how would you explain Jesus' statement that His going away would be for the good of the disciples?

John 14:16 is a very important verse for understanding the link between the Holy Spirit and Jesus. It will help to examine the two Greek words that mean "another counselor." *Parakletos* is the word translated "counselor" (or "comforter" or "helper"). It means literally, "one called alongside to help," and was sometimes used as a legal term indicating the counsel for the defense. The word is used four times in John 14-16, each time referring to the Holy Spirit. The only other occurrence of the word is in 1 John 2:1, where it refers to Jesus. *Allos* is the word for "another of the same kind." The Greek word *heteros* means "another of a different kind."

Understanding the phrase *another counselor* gives great insight into John 14:16. Jesus is saying that just as He has been the disciples' Counselor for three years, after His departure He will send another to fulfill *within* them the same role. The Holy Spirit is *like Jesus.* (Incidentally, here is the ultimate proof that the Holy Spirit is a divine Person!)

By the permanent presence of the Spirit in their lives, all believers can enjoy intimate contact with Jesus.

ASK YOURSELF: a. I have read several verses describing the relationship between the ministry of the Holy Spirit and Jesus. How can those verses help me evaluate whether or not a particular experience is a work of the Holy Spirit?
b. Am I fearful of being open to the ministry of the Holy Spirit in my life? If so, what might be wrong in my understanding of the Spirit or Jesus?

Beginning with the Spirit

7. According to the following verses, what is the work of the Holy Spirit in a person becoming a Christian?

John 16:8

1 Corinthians 12:13

Ephesians 1:13-14

BAPTISM IN THE SPIRIT: Various forms of this phrase occur in the New Testament seven times. In Matthew 3:11, Mark 1:8, Luke 3:16, and John 1:33, John the Baptist describes the contrast between his ministry (baptizing with water for repentance) and the ministry of the coming Messiah, who will baptize with the Spirit. In Acts 1:3-5 and 11:16, Jesus and the Apostle Peter refer to this event to describe what happened to the first disciples at Pentecost and the first Gentile believers. However, the rest of Acts cautions against having a beautifully precise terminology without the living experience of the Holy Spirit. In 1 Corinthians 12:13, Paul uses the term to describe the common experience of all Christians.

In light of these verses and the concept of baptism, the term is probably best used to describe immersion into the life of the Holy Spirit when a person becomes a Christian.

---

8. According to 1 Corinthians 6:19-20, what is true of every Christian?

Additional references: Acts 2:38, Romans 8:9, Galatians 4:6

Being Filled with the Spirit

9. Read Ephesians 5:18.

   a. What is God's command regarding the Holy Spirit? (The tense of the verb indicates that the action should be continual, not just one time.)

   b. What can you learn from the comparison with being drunk with wine?

"'Fill' is plainly a metaphor and it fundamentally misleads if pressed literally, as though the human objects of the Spirit's ministry were reduced to impersonal receptacles, and the blessed Spirit himself to a spiritual substance. . . . To be filled with the Spirit implies that the Spirit is the dominant influence in our behavior."[1] — BRUCE MILNE

c. Read Ephesians 5:19-21. What should be some of the consequences of being filled with the Spirit?

---

10. The Book of Acts also refers to a continual filling of the Spirit. The word used *(pleres)* implies a settled disposition in which the Spirit is the dominating influence. In the following verses, what characterizes people who are full of the Spirit?

6:3,5,8

13:52

Additional references in Acts: 7:55, 11:24

11. In Acts, another word for filled *(pimplemi)* is used for specific occasions. For example, in Acts 3:10 it describes the response of the people to a miracle: "They were filled with wonder and amazement." Look up the following references. What were the results of people being filled with the Spirit at a specific time?

2:4-11

4:31

13:9-12

Additional references in Acts: 4:8-12, 9:17-18

For Further Study
What activities of the Holy Spirit are described in the following verses in Acts?

5:30-32

9:31

10:19-23

16:6-10

20:22-24

How do these verses affect your attitude toward the Holy Spirit?

Note: The way in which the Holy Spirit equips Christians for service by giving them specific spiritual gifts is an important topic that can be studied in the book entitled *Your Part in His Plan*. If you wish to do some study now, the relevant passages are Romans 12:1-8, 1 Corinthians 12-14, Ephesians 4:7-16, and 1 Peter 4:10-11.

ASK YOURSELF: How can I allow the Holy Spirit to be a more dominating influence in my life?

Living by the Spirit

The Spirit is most commonly referred to as the *Holy* Spirit. One of His primary tasks is to enable us to grow in holiness. In this final section we will focus on this most important theme by studying Galatians 5:16-25, which is one of two New Testament passages concentrating on the practicalities of living by the Spirit. (The other passage is Romans 8:1-27.)

---

12. Read Galatians 5:16-18.

    a. What is going on within us?

    b. What hope do we have?

c. What do you think it means to be "led by the Spirit"?

d. What part do we play in this process of being led? Look also at Romans 8:12-14.

And His that gentle voice we hear,
Soft as the breath of even,
That checks each fault, that calms each fear,
And speaks of heaven.

For every virtue we posses,
And every victory won,
And every thought of holiness,
Are His alone.
HARRIET AUBER

13. Consider Galatians 5:19-23.

a. What do you think is meant by "the fruit of the Spirit"?

b. What thoughts and feelings do you have in response to these verses?

14. Read Galatians 5:24-25.

   a. According to verse 24, what did you do when you became a Christian?

   b. How should this affect your attitude from day to day? (Also see Luke 9:23.)

"The first great secret of holiness lies in the degree and decisiveness of our repentance. If besetting sins persistently plague us, it is either because we have never truly repented, or because, having repented, we have not maintained our repentance. It is as if, having hauled our old nature to the cross, we kept wistfully returning to the scene of its execution."[2] —JOHN STOTT

b. Verse 25 of Galatians 5 commands us to "keep in step with the Spirit." Literally this means, "Walk along the path the Spirit lays down." What do you think that means in practice?

c. What do the following verses teach about how to do that?

Romans 8:5

Galatians 6:7-9

ASK YOURSELF: What practical steps can I take to live more consistently by the Spirit?

Stop, Think, and Pray

What have you learned about the third Person of the Trinity? How has your appreciation of His ministry increased? How has God spoken to you about your own life? Is there anything you can do to allow the Holy Spirit to become more dominant in your life?

What I have learned

How God has spoken to me

How I need to respond

Suggested memory verse about living through God's Spirit

**So I say, live by the Spirit, and you will not gratify
the desires of the sinful nature. (Galatians 5:16)**

NOTES: 1. Bruce Milne, *Know the Truth* (Leicester, England: InterVarsity Press,
1982), page 198.
2. John Stott, *Only One Way* (Leicester, England: InterVarsity Press,
1973), pages 151-152.

Living with God's Truth

The previous lessons asked some fundamental questions: Do I
have any real significance? Do I have any value as a person, or is
my worth dependent on how successfully I live? What is the
purpose of life? We have found that the Bible provides clear
and distinctive answers. To believe its words is to develop a
framework of thinking that is in marked contrast with contemporary philosophies of life. It is to discover the truth.

This renewing of our minds with biblical truth is central to
the Spirit's work of remaking us in the image of Christ. If we
are to cooperate fully with the Spirit in His transforming activity, we need to be convinced that the Bible is indeed true. We
need to be confident that in its pages we find God's knowledge of reality and His thoughts and wishes regarding it.

In this lesson, we will examine the reasons why we can
be so confident. We will also reflect on the riches of God's
Word.

Pause for Prayer

Jesus spoke of the Holy Spirit as "the Spirit of truth" (John
14:17 and 16:13). As you investigate the subject of truth, turn
for help to the Spirit of truth, who lives within you. As you
work on the study, look to Him to inform your mind and challenge your heart.

The God Who Speaks

Modern man has largely rejected the concept of absolute truth. The word *truth* has been devalued and is used as a relative term: "It may be true for you, but it isn't true for me!"

The Bible stands against all such relativism. It does so, first, by asserting the existence of God; He is there in an absolute sense, whether or not anyone believes in Him. He is "the true God . . . the living God" (Jeremiah 10:10). Furthermore, He speaks. In His words we have truth—about God and about man.

---

1. Read Hebrews 1:1-3, then focus on verse 1.

   a. According to 2 Peter 1:20-21, how did God speak through the prophets?

   b. What relationship is there between God's activity in the world and His speaking through the prophets? See Amos 3:7.

   c. Read Job 11:7-8 and Isaiah 55:8-9. Why does God reveal Himself through the prophets?

d. In two instances, what happened to the messages God gave?

Joshua 24:26

Jeremiah 30:1-2

(These are only two among numerous similar events. Other examples are found in Exodus 24:3-4 and 34:27, Numbers 33:2, Isaiah 30:8, Daniel 7:1, and Habakkuk 2:2-3.)

_____

2. Read Hebrews 1:2-3 again.

   a. How did God speak by Jesus Christ?

   b. According to 1 John 1:1-3, what part did the apostles have in transmitting God's message?

c. According to 1 Corinthians 2:6-13, how did God make known what He was doing through the coming of Christ?

God reveals Himself in His dealings with men and nations. He reveals Himself supremely in the coming of Jesus Christ. God also speaks. He gives His own commentary on what He is doing and why. And He gives that commentary through human spokesmen.

Some people believe that it is impossible for a human author to communicate a pure message from God. The personality of the author, they say, will influence and alter God's revelation. It is true that humans do speak and write in their distinctive styles. However, we must not ignore the fact that God is the sovereign Creator. Knowing the message He wishes to communicate, there is no reason why He cannot mold the personalities of His spokesmen so that they give to His Word precisely the emphasis and expression He desires.

ASK YOURSELF: How can I praise God more often for His grace in revealing Himself to us?

The Bible as God's Word

Not everything in the Bible comes to us with the force of the words *Thus says the Lord,* although this phrase does occur nearly 4,000 times in the Old Testament. Nonetheless, the Christian view throughout history is that the entire Bible is God's Word. It is a view based on the teachings of Jesus and His apostles.

3. a. What can you learn from these references in Matthew about Jesus' attitude toward the Old Testament?

4:1-11

5:17-20

15:1-9

19:3-9

Additional references in Matthew: 11:7-10; 12:1-8; 21:12-13; 22:23-33; 22:41-46; 23:33-35; 26:23-24; 26:31; 26:52-54

b. How would you summarize Jesus' attitude toward the Old Testament?

Jesus never gave any indication that He disagreed with the Old Testament writings. On the contrary, He received them as the Word of God, quoted them as the final authority in disputes, and applied their principles.

The Old Testament

4. What do the following references in Acts reveal about the attitude of the apostles toward the Old Testament?

1:15-22

2:14-21

4:24-31

28:23-28

5. In 2 Timothy 3:14-17, how does the Apostle Paul describe the nature and value of Scripture?

"I beseech you all, weigh not what this man or that thinketh; but touching all these things search the Scriptures."

—JOHN CHRYSOSTOM*

ASK YOURSELF: How does my attitude toward the Old Testament compare with Jesus' attitude?

The New Testament

6. Consider Jesus' attitude toward His own teaching.

    a. According to Matthew 24:35, how important did He think it was?

    b. Read John 14:26. What promise does Jesus make about His teaching?

c. How should Jesus' attitude affect our attitude toward the gospels?

---

7. What promise did Jesus make in John 16:12-15?

---

8. How was Jesus' promise fulfilled?

Ephesians 3:1-5

Revelation 1:1-3 and 22:18-19

9. Into what category does Peter put Paul's writings in 2 Peter 3:15-16?

God ensured that His supreme act of revelation in the coming of Christ was recorded and interpreted. Just as in Old Testament times there were prophets raised up and inspired to witness to God's activity, so in the early Church, apostles and prophets proclaimed the Word of God. They spoke and wrote with His authority.

10. Consider Ephesians 2:19-22, especially verse 20.

   a. How are the apostles and prophets described?

   b. How does this make them unique?

   c. How should this affect our attitude toward their teaching?

THE CANON: The teaching of the apostles was—and is—regarded as inspired and authoritative. They were the teachers of "the faith." Christians were urged "to contend for the faith that was once for all entrusted to the saints" (Jude 3).

By the second century, it became necessary to distinguish the writings of the apostles from that circulated by heretical teachers. So began the process of establishing a list (or canon) of writings regarded as having the status of Scripture. The establishing of a canon did not invest any of the writings with an authority they did not previously possess; rather, it recognized their existing authority.

Most of the books in our current New Testament were beyond dispute. However, all the writings supposedly coming from the apostles (or their close associates) were checked and cross-checked for authenticity. By AD 367, the accepted list was exactly as we now have it.

As far as the Old Testament canon is concerned, the Church adopted the Hebrew Bible. Its traditional contents were almost certainly well established by the time of Christ. Other books (including the Apocrypha) were esteemed in the early Church but rarely regarded as inspired. At the time of the Reformation, the Apocrypha was accorded canonical status by the Roman Catholic Church.

"So long as your mind entertains any misgivings as to the certainty of the Word, its authority will be weak and dubious, or rather it will have no authority at all." —JOHN CALVIN*

> **ASK YOURSELF:** In what areas, if any, do I fail to recognize the Bible's authority over my life?

For Further Study

Growing assurance about the reliability of the Bible helps us place our confidence in it as God's Word. On the next page are some brief comments on the main issues.

73

Is the Bible historically accurate?

Although it was fashionable in the late eighteenth and nineteenth centuries to question much of the historicity of the Bible, archaeology has progressively reversed the trend. *Evidence that Demands a Verdict,* by Josh McDowell, gives numerous examples, and includes this impressive quote from the renowned Jewish archaeologist Nelson Glueck: "It may be stated categorically that no archaeological discovery has ever controverted a Biblical reference."[1]

Was the New Testament tradition exaggerated?

There was certainly some passage of time before events were written down. This was not a long period; most scholars now agree that almost the entire New Testament was in existence within thirty to fifty years of the death of Jesus. Nonetheless, the time gap could give rise to doubt. For that reason, several factors need to be weighed.

A. Communication in Jewish society was oral. Therefore, accurate memorization was an important feature of life.

B. Those who wrote the New Testament claimed to be eyewitnesses or to be writing from firsthand information (see Luke 1:1-4, 2 Peter 1:16, and 1 John 1:3).

C. Those doing the writing believed they were transmitting a message from God, and therefore recorded it with the utmost care.

D. We have independent yet parallel accounts of many of the events.

E. The accounts were written down within the lifetimes of eyewitnesses (see 1 Corinthians 15:6).

Has the text been corrupted?

Until recently, the oldest surviving manuscript of the Old Testament was one written about AD 900. Given its distance from the time of the events it recorded, it was reasonable to assume that this manuscript had been corrupted considerably in transmission. Among manuscripts discovered in 1947 (the

"Dead Sea Scrolls") was a complete copy of Isaiah from about 125 BC. It was almost identical to the one from AD 900! Thus, in over 1,000 years of copying, there had been virtually no corruption of the text at all.

This incredible accuracy reflects the reverence of the copyists for the Word of God. A similar accuracy is apparent in the work of those who copied the New Testament, for which we have thousands of manuscripts dating back as far as AD 130. Professor F.F. Bruce writes, "The variant readings about which any doubt remains among textual critics of the New Testament affect no material question of historic fact or of Christian faith and practice."[2]

The Riches of God's Word

Psalm 119 is an acrostic poem. It is divided into twenty-two sections, each one having eight verses. In each section, all the verses begin with the same letter of the Hebrew alphabet. (Some Bible versions clearly divide the psalm in this way.) The theme of the psalm is love for the Word of God, and it can be a great stimulus to us as we reflect upon the riches we have in the Bible.

---

11. Select any two sections of Psalm 119. (For questions a, b, and c, list more than one verse.)

    a. How does the psalmist describe God's Word? What does each description communicate about God's Word?

Verse	Description	What this communicates

Verse	Description	What this communicates

b. What does the psalmist believe God's Word can do for him?

Verse	How God's Word can help

c. What is the psalmist's attitude toward God's Word?

Verse	Attitude of the psalmist

"Divine Scripture is the feast of wisdom, and the single books are the various dishes." — AMBROSE*

ASK YOURSELF: In what ways do I need to change my attitude toward the Bible?

Stop, Think, and Pray

What have you learned about the Bible? Perhaps the lesson has helped you face some misgivings you have about the Bible being God's Word. Do you still have doubts? How can you resolve them?

Or perhaps the lesson has underlined the confidence you already have in God's Word. Maybe God has spoken to you in other ways about your attitude toward the Bible. Has the example of Jesus been a challenge? Have you been stirred by the attitudes of the apostles or the psalmist? Does God want you to change as a result of this study? Are there any actions you need to take? Are there some attitudes you need to develop?

Main lessons

My response

Scripture memory verse about living with God's truth

**All Scripture is God-breathed and is useful for teaching, rebuking, correcting and training in righteousness, so that the man of God may be thoroughly equipped for every good work.
(2 Timothy 3:16-17)**

NOTES: 1. Josh McDowell, *Evidence that Demands a Verdict* (San Bernardino, California: Here's Life Publishers, Inc., 1972), page 65.
2. F.F. Bruce, *The New Testament Documents: Are They Reliable?* (Grand Rapids, Michigan: Eerdmans Publishing Company, 1960), pages 19-20.

Living Out God's Truth

In the previous lesson, we grappled with a fundamental issue: Is the Bible the Word of God? Is it true and trustworthy? Is it an unqualified expression of God's mind? The answers to these questions are of great importance for our lives.

It is possible to answer yes to all these questions and still fail to live in conscious submission to the Bible. Many people who claim to be Bible-believing Christians demonstrate remarkable ignorance of the Bible's teaching. Others show an inability to translate biblical knowledge into a biblical lifestyle. It is God's purpose to renew our minds with His truth, and by so doing, to transform our lives. In this lesson we will examine our part in this process and some of the potential pitfalls.

Pause for Prayer

How did you respond to the "Ask Yourself" question on page 77? Take a moment to express to God what you want your attitude toward the Bible to be.

Knowing the Truth

The Bible is a collection of 66 books written over a period of some 1,500 years. Although written on 3 continents by over 40 authors in 3 languages, it displays remarkable unity. The diagram on the next page gives a simple overview. (It is worth the effort to memorize the order of the books for easy reference in the years to come. It is not as hard as it might appear! Try the New Testament first.)

OLD TESTAMENT (39 books)

LAW (5 books)	HISTORY (12 books)	POETRY AND WISDOM (5 books)	PROPHECY (17 books)
Genesis	Joshua	Job	**Major Prophets**
Exodus	Judges	Psalms	Isaiah
Leviticus	Ruth	Proverbs	Jeremiah
Numbers	1 Samuel	Ecclesiastes	Lamentations
Deuteronomy	2 Samuel	Song of Solomon	Ezekiel
	1 Kings		Daniel
	2 Kings		
	1 Chronicles		**Minor Prophets**
	2 Chronicles		Hosea
	Ezra		Joel
	Nehemiah		Amos
	Esther		Obadiah
			Jonah
			Micah
			Nahum
			Habakkuk
			Zephaniah
			Haggai
			Zechariah
			Malachi

About 400 years between Testaments

The Old Testament looks forward to Christ's sacrifice on the Cross.

The New Testament is based on the work Christ finished on the Cross.

NEW TESTAMENT (27 books)

GOSPELS (4 books)	HISTORY (1 book)	LETTERS (21 books)	END TIMES (1 book)
Matthew	Acts	**Paul's Letters**	Revelation
Mark		Romans	
Luke		1 Corinthians	
John		2 Corinthians	
		Galatians	
		Ephesians	
		Philippians	
		Colossians	
		1 Thessalonians	
		2 Thessalonians	
		1 Timothy	
		2 Timothy	
		Titus	
		Philemon	
		General Letters	
		Hebrews	
		James	
		1 Peter	
		2 Peter	
		1 John	
		2 John	
		3 John	
		Jude	

"The New is the Old concealed. The Old is in the New revealed."
— AUGUSTINE*

Throughout the Old Testament there are commands to know the Word of God. There are also inspiring examples of people who obeyed those commands.

---

1. What can you learn from the following passages?

Deuteronomy 6:4-9

Deuteronomy 17:18-20

Proverbs 22:17-19

2. What inspiration can you gain from the following examples?

    Ezra 7:8-10

    Psalm 119:9-11

    Jeremiah 15:16 and 20:9

3. Jesus also emphasized the importance of knowing and obeying the Word of God. What does He teach in the following verses?

    Matthew 4:4

Matthew 22:29

Luke 8:19-21 and 11:27

ASK YOURSELF: Which of the verses in questions 1-3 has most inspired me to get to know the Bible, and why?

Getting a Grasp of the Bible

The passages in questions 1-3 refer to various ways of getting to know the Bible. The fingers of the hand represent five ways in which we can become familiar with the Word of God. As we take full advantage of each of these, our grasp of the Bible becomes more firm.

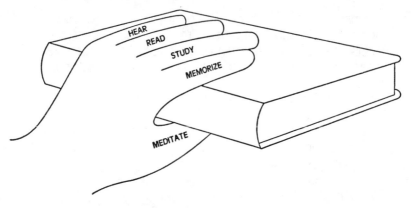

HEAR
READ
STUDY
MEMORIZE
MEDITATE

**"You have exalted above all things
your name and your word." (Psalm 138:2)**

Hear

Listen to the Bible as it is explained by gifted teachers or as it is communicated informally in fellowship. (The biblical basis can be found in Ephesians 4:11-12 and Colossians 3:16. For examples, see Acts 2:42 and Nehemiah 8:5-18.) This is a very important form of intake, ensuring we maintain a balanced view of Scripture. It also corrects faulty interpretations and develops our Christian understanding in ways we had not considered. Before you hear God's Word, ask Him to make you receptive.

Read

As well as reading a portion of the Bible each day in your "quiet time," there is great value in systematically reading through the Bible. (The biblical basis is 2 Timothy 3:16. Examples are found in Luke 24:27 and Deuteronomy 17:18-20.)

Reading need not involve detailed study; it can give a perspective on God and His ways that is sometimes lost in our attention to detail. Many find this type of reading a great joy and stimulus to fellowship with God. An easy-to-read version of the Bible is important. Pace yourself by setting a goal. For example, by reading five chapters a week, you would complete the New Testament in a year. By reading three chapters a day and five on Sundays, you would finish the whole Bible in a year.

Study

Personal study of the Bible is essential if you are to gain real convictions. (The biblical basis is 2 Timothy 2:15. See examples in Acts 17:11 and Ezra 7:10.) This *Learning to Live Bible Study Series* should lay the foundation on which you can build your own Bible study program.

The important thing in Bible study is not to look for superficial thoughts, but for the objective truths of Scripture. In time, you will want to learn to check your own understanding against the writings of Bible teachers. Group discussion of your findings can also be a great benefit.

Memorize

For the time invested, memorizing Scripture yields great benefits. It is one very practical way of making sure that God's

Word is continuously available to you. (The biblical basis is Deuteronomy 6:6-7 and Proverbs 27:17-19. Examples are given in Matthew 4:1-11 and Psalm 119:9-11.)

The key to success is to have a workable system. On pages 113-114 you will find some guidelines.

Meditate

Meditation is prayerful reflection on a verse or passage with a view to understanding and putting into practice what the Bible teaches. Rather than being one more form of intake, meditation is the essential accompaniment to all the others. Just as it is hard to physically hold a Bible without using your thumb, so it is hard to grasp God's Word without meditating on it. The third section of this lesson, "Meditating on the Truth," develops this subject.

It is important to make a distinction between biblical meditation and techniques such as transcendental meditation, yoga, and the like. These find their inspiration in Eastern religions and are often quite contrary to the practice described in the Bible.

"Apply yourself to the whole text, and apply the whole text to yourself." —JOHANN BENGEL*

We are apt to forget how privileged we are to have the Bible readily available in our own language. Church history witnesses to the price paid by those who have translated and preserved it for us. But even today, thousands of language groups still await a Bible in their own tongue.

ASK YOURSELF: How can I strengthen my intake of God's Word?

Obeying the Truth

4. Read about the wise man and the foolish man in Matthew 7:24-27.

a. What do they have in common?

b. How do they differ?

c. What warning does this passage give?

d. What encouragement does it offer?

To increase your interaction with God's Word, use the acronym SPECK. As you read a verse or a passage, ask these questions:

Is there a **S**in to avoid?
Is there a **P**romise to claim?
Is there an **E**xample to follow?
Is there a **C**ommand to obey?
Is there some new **K**nowledge about God?

Jay Adams, a Christian counselor, writes, "One may not sit waiting for the proper feelings before obeying the Word of God; he must obey regardless of how he feels. Often doing leads to proper feeling."[1] We may wonder if such a decision of the will is "being ourselves." The issue is whether we want to be our old selves or our new selves!

Behind a wrong feeling there often lies a wrong thought, attitude, or assumption about life. We should not obey wrong feelings, but we should try to understand the cause, and then change what is wrong. The last section in this lesson, "The Renewed Mind," touches on this process.

ASK YOURSELF: What hinders me the most from living in obedience to God's Word?

For Further Study

Read through 1 Samuel 15. What can you learn about obedience from this chapter? Where does Saul go wrong? What does his attitude reveal? What is God's response? How does Samuel describe disobedience?

Meditating on the Truth

5. The Bible is God's Word; it is objective truth. Therefore, we must work to understand it and see its relevance.

   a. How does 1 Corinthians 2:12 and 14 bring this out? (In the context of verse 13, verse 12 applies primarily to the apostles. It does, however, have a secondary application to all Christians.)

   b. How should this truth affect our approach to the Bible?

6. Consider Joshua 1:7-9.

   a. What did God command Joshua to do?

b. What did God promise him?

In his book *Knowing God,* J.I. Packer writes, "Meditation is the activity of calling to mind, and thinking over, and dwelling on, and applying to oneself, the various things that one knows about the works and ways and purposes and promises of God."[2]

Think about the following phrases:

calling to mind—Meditation is a deliberate decision to think about the truths of God's Word. It is not daydreaming.

thinking over—It involves effort. Nothing is so easy as thinking, but nothing is so hard as thinking well.

dwelling on—Meditation is an unhurried exercise. There are no shortcuts to Christian maturity.

applying to oneself—The aim is always to see the personal implications and to act on them.

Meditation is an intensely spiritual activity. Packer describes it as "an activity of holy thought, consciously performed in the presence of God, under the eye of God, by the help of God, as a means of communion with God."[3]

---

7. As a practical exercise, we are going to meditate on Jesus' words in John 8:31-32. Pause to ask God the Holy Spirit to enlighten your understanding as you consider these verses. As you follow the steps, record any observations you have.

Call to mind
  a. Look at the context (John 8:12-59). In what circum-
     stances did Jesus make this statement?

  b. Read verses 31 and 32 several times. You may even want
     to memorize them.

Think it over
  c. Identify and define key words and phrases (for example,
     believed, hold to, disciples).

  d. Paraphrase the verses (that is, write them in your own
     words). Or read them in a paraphrased version, such as
     The Living Bible.

e. Ask questions about who, what, when, why, and how: To whom did Jesus say this? How might they have been feeling? What did He promise them? How does truth bring freedom?

Dwell on
  f. Emphasize different words or phrases: *if* you hold to my teaching; if you *hold* to my teaching; if you hold to *my* teaching.

  g. Do you know any helpful cross-references? Can you find any in the margin of your Bible?

Apply to oneself

h. Ask yourself some questions: How am I holding to Christ's teaching? Do I believe obedience brings freedom? How can I more fully experience the truth of these verses?

i. Make plans for personal application: What should I do? How? When?

"In God's presence I open His book. . . . Does anything appear dark and intricate? I lift up my heart to the Father of Lights. . . . I then search after and consider parallel passages. . . . I meditate thereon. . . . If any doubt still remains I consult those who are experienced in the things of God, and then the writings whereby, being dead, they yet speak." —JOHN WESLEY*

ASK YOURSELF: How can I make my meditation on God's Word more effective?

The Renewed Mind

In this final section, we will focus on Romans 12:2:

*Do not conform any longer to the pattern of this world, but
be transformed by the renewing of your mind. Then you will
be able to test and approve what God's will is—
his good, pleasing and perfect will.*

---

8. "Do not conform any longer to the pattern of this world."

   a. What are some of the ways in which the world exerts its
   pressure on us?

   b. What additional insight do you find in John 8:44 and
   Ephesians 2:1-2?

c. What can you do to resist conformity?

9. "But be transformed by the renewing of your mind."

a. How does God renew your mind?

b. Read the following quotation. On which of the subjects listed have your views been changed by your understanding of God's Word? Underline them.

"We must ask ourselves, Where did I get my opinions on everything: finances, success, marriage, child raising, business, time use, sex, people, pleasure, education, progress, society, sports, politics, organization, and religion? Did any of my beliefs come, in fact, from God's Word?"[4] — Jim Petersen

c. In what area of life are you most in need of a biblical perspective at this time?

---

10. "Then you will be able to test and approve what God's will is—his good, pleasing and perfect will."

How does this statement affect your desire to obey God?

"Study therefore, I pray thee, and daily meditate on the words of the Creator. Learn the mind of God in the Word of God."
— GREGORY THE GREAT*

ASK YOURSELF: What changes do I need to make to ensure I am not conforming to the world's pattern?

Stop, Think, and Pray

How has God spoken to me through this lesson? In what ways can I strengthen the impact of His word on my life? Which one does God want me to put into practice right away? How do I plan to do it?

REMEMBER

Scripture memory verse about living out God's truth

Do not let this Book of the Law depart from your mouth; meditate on it day and night, so that you may be careful to do everything written in it. Then you will be prosperous and successful.
(Joshua 1:8)

NOTES: 1. Jay Adams, *Christian Counselor's Manual* (Grand Rapids, Michigan: Baker Book House, 1979), page 131.
2. J.I. Packer, *Knowing God* (Downers Grove, Illinois: InterVarsity Press, 1973), pages 18-19.
3. Packer, page 19.
4. Jim Petersen, *Evangelism as a Lifestyle* (Colorado Springs, Colorado: NavPress, 1981), page 79.

Living as God's People

To this point, we have concentrated on the individual dimension of God's salvation. This is only one side of the story, however. It is God's nature to relate to others; He is Himself a perfect unity of three distinguishable Persons. Since man is made in the image of God, man reflects this social nature. God Himself said, "It is not good for the man to be alone" (Genesis 2:18). God's creation plan, then, was for individuals to live and develop within the context of loving relationships with other human beings.

The Fall, however, caused a breakdown in man's relationship with God. This immediately affected man's relationships with others. The first murder is recorded in Genesis 4, and thereafter, society is characterized by conflict, exploitation, fear, and misunderstanding. This is not the whole story, of course, for there are still many examples of love and loyalty and cooperation. But even the closest human relationships are affected by sin.

Nevertheless, God is at work to rescue us from the effects of the Fall. In Christ, He has redeemed a *people*. We are chosen not only as individuals, but as a corporate body. Ultimately, we will glorify God *together* in Heaven. In the meantime, God is at work to renew relationships among His people. Our fellowship as Christians is intended to be an example to the world of the new society that God will bring into being.

Pause for Prayer

God wants to renew our minds and our lifestyles through the instrument of His Word. However, Satan is actively trying to make us neglect this priceless Book. If he fails in that, his next device is to prevent us from understanding its personal relevance. If he fails in that, his final strategy is to make us satisfied merely with good intentions. Only by God's help can we complete each lesson and then live out the truths. Pray as you study that the result of these hours in God's Word will be a changed lifestyle.

The People of God

1. As described in Titus 2:11-14 and Revelation 21:1-3, what was God's ultimate purpose in sending Christ?

2. Acts 15 describes a meeting ("the Council of Jerusalem") called to discuss the Christian mission to the Gentiles. Read verses 5-18.

    a. According to verse 14, what had God been doing through this mission?

b. Consider verses 15-18. How did God's work among the Gentiles relate to what He had previously been doing with Old Testament Israel? (From the time of King David, Israel was often referred to as "the house of David.")

c. In verses 7-11, the Apostle Peter opposes the view of the Pharisees that to be full members of the people of God, the Gentiles must convert to Judaism (see verse 5). What are Peter's reasons for insisting that all Christians—Jews and Gentiles—belong to the same people of God?

Ephesians 2:11-22 is an illuminating cross-reference to this passage in Acts. If you have time, read this passage and notice the way in which God has created *one* people from both Jews and Gentiles.

"God chose the children of Israel, redeeming them from Egypt, saying, 'I will take you for my people, and I will be your God' (Exodus 6:7; compare Deuteronomy 7:6). This theme echoes consistently through the Old Testament. Moving into the New Testament, we learn that the people of God find its center and basis in Jesus Christ. The unfaithfulness of God's people in the Old Testament did not thwart God's plan. God is still calling out and preparing his people, not principally the biological Israel but the new and true Israel, the church."[1] — HOWARD SNYDER

3. What do the following references reveal about Jesus' concerns for the developing Christian community?

John 13:34-35

John 17:20-23

ASK YOURSELF: In my attitudes toward other Christians, how can I reflect the truth that we belong to the *one* people of God?

Attitudes for Unity

The Greek word for fellowship is *koinonia*. Its primary meaning is "sharing in common." Christians share in common their Lord, their possession of the Spirit, and their faith. It is because all Christians have this (vertical) relationship that they also have (horizontal) fellowship with fellow believers.

4. Colossians 3:12-14 lists some attitudes that are important if fellowship is to flourish. List them in the chart on the following page and explain what each one means in practical terms. Mark with an asterisk the *one* that is particularly relevant to you at this time.

Attitude	What this means

5. Many offenses that Christians commit against one another can, in love, be forgiven and forgotten. Sometimes, however, a wrong can drive a wedge between Christians. The Bible gives clear guidelines on how to deal with such conflict. What principles can you find in the following passages in Matthew?

5:21-24

18:15-17

18:21-22

___

6. Read 2 Corinthians 13:12. Keep in mind that the particular form of greeting is largely cultural.

    a. Is there a Christian you see regularly who you find difficult to greet warmly?

    b. What can you do to change your attitude?

PORTLOCK

"I'd like to thank the board for this lovely plant,
especially after our disagreement this week."

ASK YOURSELF: a. Do I have any unresolved conflict with a fellow Christian? If so, what do I need to do to resolve it? b. What attitudes do I have toward Christians that could hinder my fellowship with them?

For Further Study

Read Romans 14:1-15:9. What does this passage teach about relating to a fellow Christian with whom you disagree? What contemporary issues do you see as the equivalents of those described by Paul? In what ways do you need to change your attitude(s)?

Patterns for Fellowship

7. What can you discover in Acts 2:42-47 about the fellowship of the early Church?

This depth of involvement in the lives of others drew its inspiration from the example of Jesus' commitment to His twelve disciples and His life with them.

"How inexhaustible are the riches that open up for those who by God's will are privileged to live in the daily fellowship of life with other Christians." — DIETRICH BONHOEFFER*

8. The New Testament gives a number of pictures of the Church. These pictures can help us appreciate more fully what God desires in our fellowship. Listed on pages 106 and 107 are four pictures used in Ephesians. For each one, there is a cross-reference and a question to stimulate your thoughts about what the picture teaches regarding fellowship. (You may wish to use cross-references and questions of your own, instead.)

a. God's household (Ephesians 2:19 and 1 Timothy 3:14-15)
   Cross-reference: 1 John 5:1
   How do members of a family relate in a good way?

b. God's temple (Ephesians 2:20-22 and 1 Corinthians
   3:16-17)
   Cross-reference: 1 Peter 2:4-5
   What kind of a building does God want?

c. Body of Christ (Ephesians 4:11-16 and 1 Corinthians
   12:27)
   Cross-reference: Romans 12:4-8
   How does a body function?

d. Bride of Christ (Ephesians 5:25-32 and Revelation 19:6-8)
Cross-reference: 2 Corinthians 11:2-3
How can we help one another get ready for our marriage to Christ?

ASK YOURSELF: Which of the New Testament pictures of the Church most motivates me about fellowship, and why?

True Biblical Fellowship

9. What do the following Old Testament references illustrate about fellowship?

Proverbs 27:17

Ecclesiastes 4:9-10

10. Listed below and on page 109 are seven New Testament commands regarding our fellowship with other Christians. For each reference, write what we are to do, and then explain what this means in practice.

Galatians 6:1

Galatians 6:2

Galatians 6:6

Colossians 3:16

Hebrews 3:12-13

Hebrews 10:23-25

James 5:16

"It is not a good sign when a person recognizes no difference between [eating] sweets and eating a square meal. Equally, it is not a good sign when Christians recognize no difference between social activities in Christian company and fellowship."[2]

—J.I. PACKER

11. According to 1 John 1:3-7, what is the link between our fellowship with one another and our fellowship with God?

ASK YOURSELF: **a.** Which Christian(s) am I relating to in the depth indicated in the passages for this section? **b.** What can I do to seek out or strengthen fellowship with other Christians?

Stop, Think, and Pray

What have you learned about the corporate life of Christians? What discoveries have you made about the nature and practice of Christian fellowship? How has God spoken to you? Perhaps you have become aware of needs in the Christian group of which you are a member. Make note of these.

How my group needs to change

What I can do about this

Changes in groups usually begin with changes in individuals. Now consider the personal implications of this lesson.

How I need to change

What I am going to do

Scripture memory verse about living as God's people

**And let us consider how we may spur one another
on toward love and good deeds. Let us not give up
meeting together, as some are in the habit of
doing, but let us encourage one another—and all
the more as you see the Day approaching.
(Hebrews 10:24-25)**

===

NOTES: 1. Howard Snyder, *New Wineskins* (London: Marshall Morgan & Scott, 1975), page 91.
2. J.I. Packer, *God's Words* (Leicester, England: InterVarsity Press, 1981), page 191.

Memorizing Scripture

As You Start to Memorize a Verse

1. Read in your Bible the context of each verse you memorize.
2. Try to gain a clear understanding of what each verse actually means. (You may want to read the verse in other Bible translations or paraphrases to get a better grasp of the meaning.)
3. Read the verse several times thoughtfully, aloud or in a whisper. This will help you grasp the verse as a whole. Each time you read it, say the topic, reference, verse, and then the reference again.
4. Discuss the verse with God in prayer, and continue to seek His help for success in Scripture memory.

While You Are Memorizing a Verse

5. Work on saying the verse aloud as much as possible.
6. Learn the topic and reference first.
7. After learning the topic and reference, learn the first phrase of the verse. Once you have learned the topic, reference, and first phrase and have repeated them several times, continue adding more phrases, one at a time.
8. Think about how the verse applies to you and your daily circumstances.
9. Always include the topic and reference as part of the verse as you learn it and review it.

After You Have Memorized a Verse

10. Write the verse from memory and check your accuracy. This deepens the impression in your mind.
11. Review the verse immediately after learning it, and repeat it frequently in the next few days. This is crucial for getting the verse firmly fixed in your mind, because of how quickly we tend to forget what we have recently learned.
12. REVIEW! REVIEW! REVIEW! Repetition is the best way to engrave the verse on your memory.

Who's Who

Below, listed in alphabetical order, are brief biographical sketches of the figures from the history of the Church who are quoted in this book.

Ambrose (339-397)
Roman governor of part of northern Italy when he was chosen as Bishop of Milan by popular acclamation. As a bishop, his life was one of ceaseless activity directed to preaching, to works of charity, and to the defense of the Church against heretical influences. He also vigorously asserted the Church's authority against the state.

Augustine of Hippo (354-430)
The son of a pagan father and Christian mother, he was born and educated in North Africa. Following a dissolute lifestyle, he moved to Italy and became professor of logic in Milan. There, in 386, he was converted to Christianity. Returning to North Africa, he became Bishop of Hippo and one of the great writers and theologians of the Western Church.

Bengel, Johann (1687-1752)
German Lutheran theologian and commentator. A devoted Bible student, he pioneered the science of textual criticism, wrote a commentary on the New Testament, and influenced many German preachers by his godliness and sound learning.

Bonhoeffer, Dietrich (1906-1945)
German Lutheran minister and author. A strong opponent of the Nazis, he was imprisoned in 1943 and hanged shortly before the end of the war.

Calvin, John (1509-1564)
French reformer and theologian. He was converted in 1533 while a student in Paris. He linked up with Protestants and later became a leader of the Reformation in Geneva. His *Institutes of the Christian Religion* became the guide of the Reformed churches.

Chrysostom, John (354-407)
Monk from Antioch who became Patriarch of Constantinople. An outstanding orator, his godliness and reforming zeal resulted in his ill-treatment, exile, and death.

Gregory the Great (540-604)
From a Roman noble family. He entered a monastery and rose to become the first monk Bishop of Rome in 590. A great organizer and diplomat, he initiated the mission to England under Augustine (of Canterbury).

Newman, John Henry (1801-1890)
Born in London and reared in an evangelical home. In 1828 he became vicar of the Anglican university church in Oxford. In 1845 he joined the Roman Catholic Church, became a priest and later a cardinal.

Wesley, John (1703-1791)
A great preacher of the English evangelical revival. Although already a Church of England minister, he came to a living faith in 1738. Prevented from speaking in churches, he traveled some 250,000 miles and preached some 40,000 sermons in the open air. He organized the converts into classes and societies, which developed into the Methodist Church after his death.

For Further Reading

1. Living as God Intends
Milne, Bruce, *Know the Truth*, InterVarsity Press
Stott, John R.W., *Men Made New: An Exposition of Romans 5-8*, Baker Book House

2. Living by God's Grace
Packer, J.I., *God's Words*, InterVarsity Press
Packer, J.I., *Knowing God*, InterVarsity Press

3. Living Through God's Spirit
Green, Michael, *I Believe in the Holy Spirit*, Eerdmans Publishing Company
Lloyd-Jones, David M., *Life in the Spirit*, Baker Book House
Milne, Bruce, *Know the Truth*, InterVarsity Press

4. Living with God's Truth
McDowell, Josh, *Evidence that Demands a Verdict*, Here's Life Publishers
Milne, Bruce, *Know the Truth*, InterVarsity Press
Packer, J.I., *God Has Spoken*, InterVarsity Press
Packer, J.I., *God's Words*, InterVarsity Press
Schaeffer, Francis, *He Is There and He Is Not Silent*, Tyndale House Publishers

5. Living Out God's Truth

Appointment with God, NavPress

Henrichsen, Walter, *A Layman's Guide to Interpreting the Bible*, Zondervan Pubishing House

Sanchez, George, *Changing Your Thought Patterns*, NavPress (booklet)

6. Living as God's People

Milne, Bruce, *We Belong Together*, InterVarsity Press

Packer, J.I., *God's Words*, InterVarsity Press